Best Wishes
Mister Flick

the
WISH
POST

BY

MISTER FINCH

The Wish Post
© 2018 Mister Finch

Photography and story by Mister Finch
Layout and design by Graham Pilling / Army of Cats Creative Studio

ISBN 9781527224315

First printing in the United Kingdom 2018.

www.mister-finch.com

CONTENTS:

Please Read!

Hello there dear reader and welcome to the world of The Wish Post.

We animals are normally very secretive but my friend Mister Finch has decided he trusts you! – and any friend of his is a friend of mine.

My story is told without words. If you want to follow along with my journey, you should probably read the introduction on the next page – it will help explain a few things and save me having to answer any silly questions!

AN INTRODUCTION TO THE WISH POST
by *Mister Finch*

All the creatures in all the world - all the insects, all the cats and all the dogs, all the birds, and even all those strange fish at the bottom of the ocean - can grant wishes.

You didn't know? That's okay, not many people do.

It's one of those things where once you know, you look at them all differently.

Admittedly, some will grant wishes quicker and easier than others. Butterflies and moths are very good at this, whilst cats... well, if you have a cat you will know, they can be a bit tricky. They do have the ability to grant wishes... but often it's just a case that they can't be bothered. That's cats for you.

Like most things in heaven and earth, wishes are governed by a law: a creature cannot wish for itself or for any creature it knows...

However.

There is 'The Wish Post'.

Once a year... or maybe it's every few years... a creature may make a wish.

A wish is spoken into an envelope, sealed, and then dropped off in a special post box. Scattered around the world these post-boxes are hidden out of sight and, more often than not, take the form of a toadstool (sea creatures apparently have a different one but this is yet to be confirmed).

You may have seen one and not even known - perhaps stepped over one, or even walked or driven past one on your way to work or school. There are no maps of where they are but if you know where to look, you may find a sign... or indeed actually find one!

Once a wish is left in the tiny drawer, they are collected by badgers (not always, but mostly) as they work quickly, can carry lots of mail, and are happy to work at night whilst you are tucked up in your bed.

The collected wishes are then taken to a sorting office. These are run by rats (not always, but mostly), as they are very fast workers - their nimble paws make quick work of organising - and they work exceptionally well as a team.

The next task is to take all the wishes and sew them together in long strands. Squirrels do this (not always, but mostly) as they are fast stitchers and can easily hang them in trees, which is where they end up.

And there hang all the wishes; all the dreams; all the hopes... all tightly folded in their paper homes. Now the Wish Post Festival begins and the creatures celebrate and hope. Bells ring and flags fly in anticipation of the arrival of the wind - for it's the wind, you see, who takes the wishes and it's her who grants them.

However, some things in life can be fickle and the wind is no exception.

While the creatures sleep off their Festival celebrations... the wind arrives.

Nobody has seen her but if you are lucky, you might see her hands. You may have seen them robbing the winter trees of their leaves or pulling the sheets from the washing line of a tired wife.

Tonight though, she will take only wishes. Sometimes she takes all of them - imagine, everyone getting their wish and everyone being happy. Other times she takes only a few. I told you she was fickle.

In the morning if a creature's tiny envelope has gone, they have been lucky.

But if their wish remains, they must understand that it's simply not the right time and that the wind knows best.

I know what you might be thinking - will the Wish Post work for me?

Well, humans don't need wishing post boxes, or busy badgers, or organised squirrels... they never have. They simply need the wind (even a light breeze will do) and the ability to believe that if they ask and keep their face turned to the sky, their wishes will come true.

All creatures know this... and that's why dogs wink and cats just can't be bothered.

That's cats for you.

And so
our story
begins...

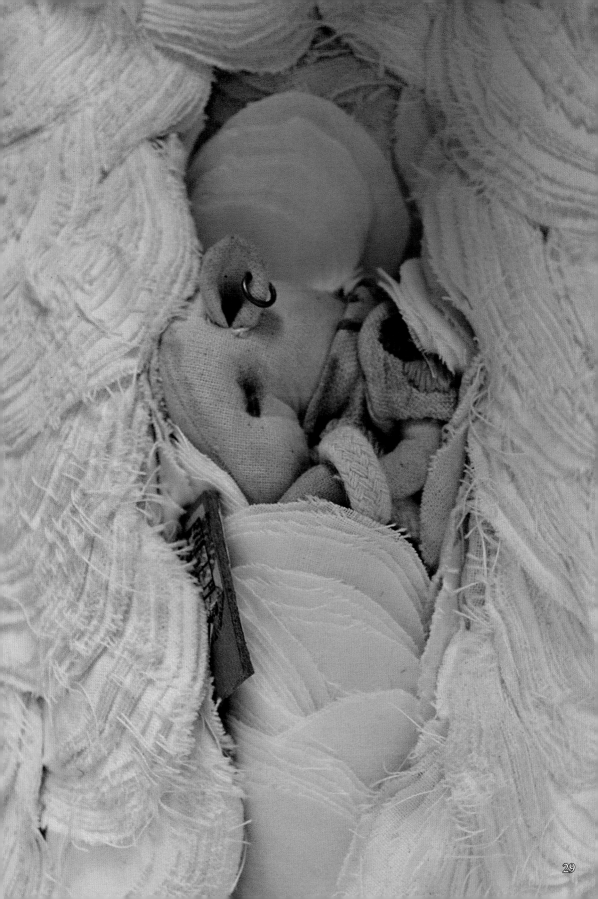

41

the
end

Behind the Scenes

....

*Badgers, Foxes, Hares,
Hedgehogs, Mice, Moles,
Moths, Rabbits, Rats,
Squirrels, Swans,
& Toadstools*

Ah, my old friends, the Badgers. These grandfatherly figures, although grumpy looking, are of course very kind.

To capture them in their natural habitat, they needed to stand independently, without being attached to a base. Making them life-size made this a tall order.

They have jackets covered in badges which show the places they have worked. These are made from the ends of souvenir spoons, each cut, filed and awarded to our trusted employees. I did go a bit mad and probably have around 500 spares - I just couldn't stop collecting them!

I imagine they start work in the early evening - slowly, steadily, nocturnally they carry their jam-packed wooden postboxes to the sorting office.

I am hugely sentimental over my trusted Badgers and love these dear souls.

Some foxes might be sly customers but these are all round great guys. Strong and able to manage jobs requiring heavy lifting, they are a huge help in moving and arranging things for the Festival. Standing on their hind legs they can even reach the highest places, where the letters are hung.

I made their little jackets from vintage tapestries. I originally wanted the Foxes trussed up with parcels but they just stood a little too precariously. Using thick wire and draughts pieces for their joints I was able to better manage their balance.

2. Foxes

Sometimes it's better to put things
away for a while so you can come back
later to look at them with fresh eyes.
This was certainly the case for my trio
of Hares.

According to the story, they carry
the rarest of the toadstools - how
important!

Their jackets are heavily trimmed
with miniature brass envelopes and
tinkling bells, so you can definitely
hear this auspicious threesome
coming.

3.
Hares

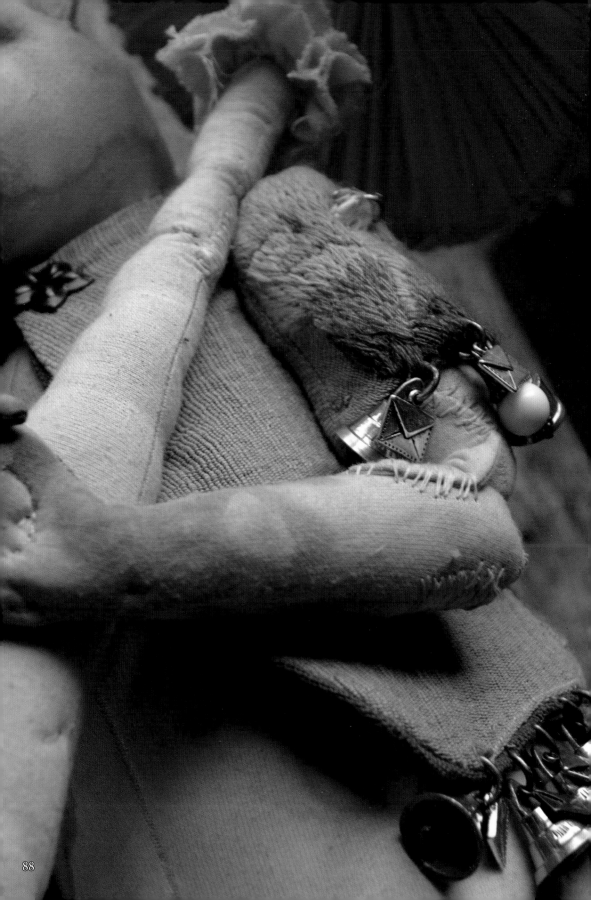

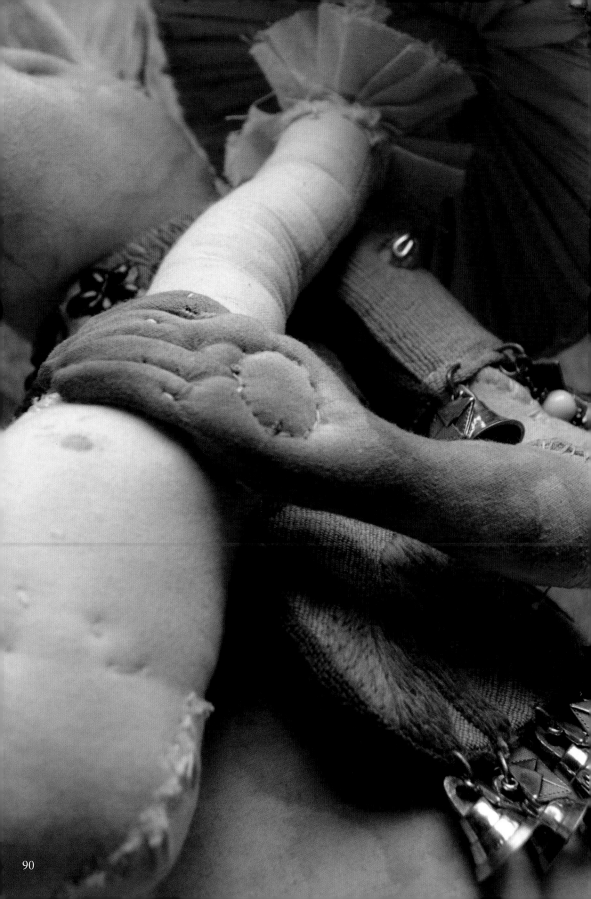

4. Hedgehogs

I wanted to make a Hedgehog band for the longest time, so allow me to introduce 'The Ring A Dings'! They have a reputation for being a little snooty and full of their own importance but rightly so, as they do help keep the time with their wonderful vintage brass bells and tiny pocket watches.

Inserting their prickly spines was quite a task and seemed to take forever, though it was worth it for the end result which has a certain realistic charm, don't you think?

While taking 'behind the scenes' shots, I happened to take a close-up which I loved so much it ended up becoming the cover.

The Festival Mice lead the procession ahead of the King. Some carry flags and bells in celebration, while others hold small offerings and gifts for The Wind.

There are 18 in total and they seem happiest sticking together in little groups. I found while creating them, that playing around with something as simple as how they stood was enough to bring out their individual personalities and moods, making each one unique.

Working small doesn't always mean less work - in fact it often means quite the opposite!

Poe the Mouse - I've lived with this darling little mouse for two years now. The lead for my story was always going to be a mouse and worked so well interacting with other characters, conveying the visuals in a way that showed the scale and proportions of everything. I had to make a few versions for the different poses I needed for the images but I loved staging everything with them.

I miss Poe being around. They were always out on my desk or in my bag in case I wanted to take a quick snap. Its almost like a strange kind of mourning - once the images were all done and I had finished, I was quite sad. Maybe they will return one day with a new adventure? I made Poe's gender non-specific so that the story could be relatable to anyone.

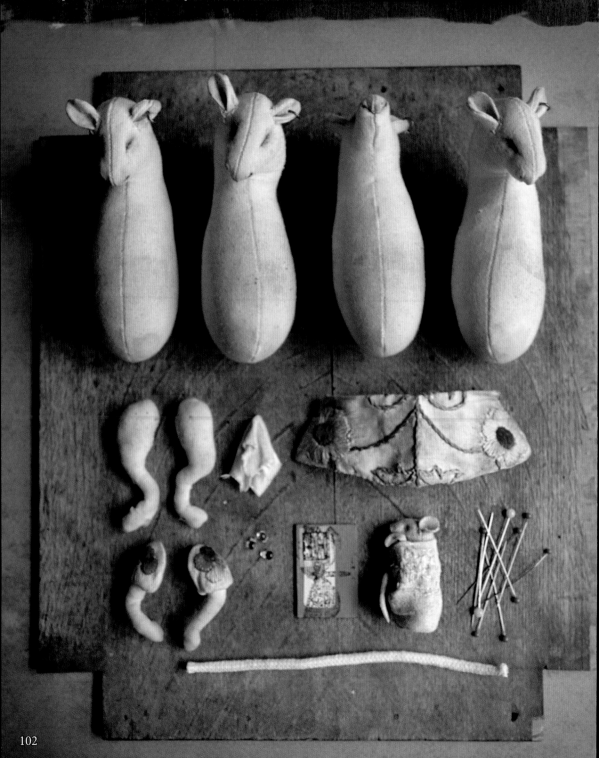

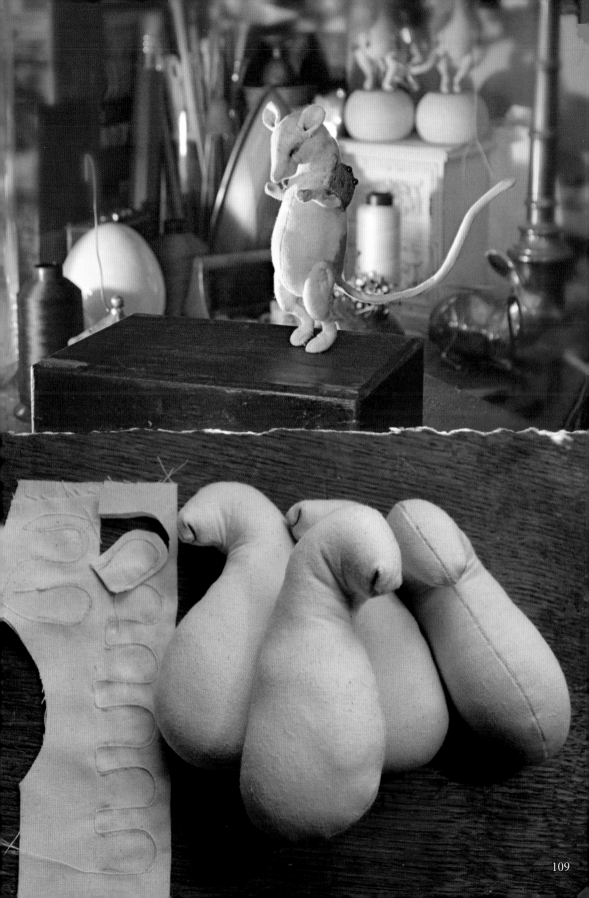

The moles keep themselves very busy, so can be a bit nervy and temperamental - but deep down, they honestly are good guys...

It was tricky working out how to make them stand on their tiptoes without losing their balance - no mean feat while carrying backpacks of precious rocks and stones. I collected so many amber beads to fill their packs, I still have a full treasure chest at home. I'm sure they'll come in handy, someday...

My finishing touch for our underground friends is the addition of the Crescent Moon buttons. As soon as I found them I knew they were perfect - after all, Moles just love the dark.

6.

Moles

7. MOTHS

I found a very pretty pair of needlework pieces, which turned out to be quite marvellous as wings for the Moths.

I have made plenty of moths before, as you may well know, and in the past I've had them carrying things and even pulling tiny brass coaches.

By getting the scale just right, the Moths were perfect for carrying a certain little mouse...

Tricky to set the scene for a photograph but with a little digital magic, Poe is whizzing through the air. Wonderful.

8. Rabbits

The Rabbits are excitable party organisers with fabulous skills in decoration. Strangely enough, while they were some of the first creatures I made, you might not spot them in the story - perhaps they were keeping busy behind the scenes, instead...

They each have fancy coats, made from a huge wall tapestry. With a multitude of different stitches and threads, someone had once spent so much time creating this beautiful piece but it had been left to gather dust in a second-hand shop. When I rescued it, I knew at once that the bright, landscape imagery would make it perfect for my Rabbits.

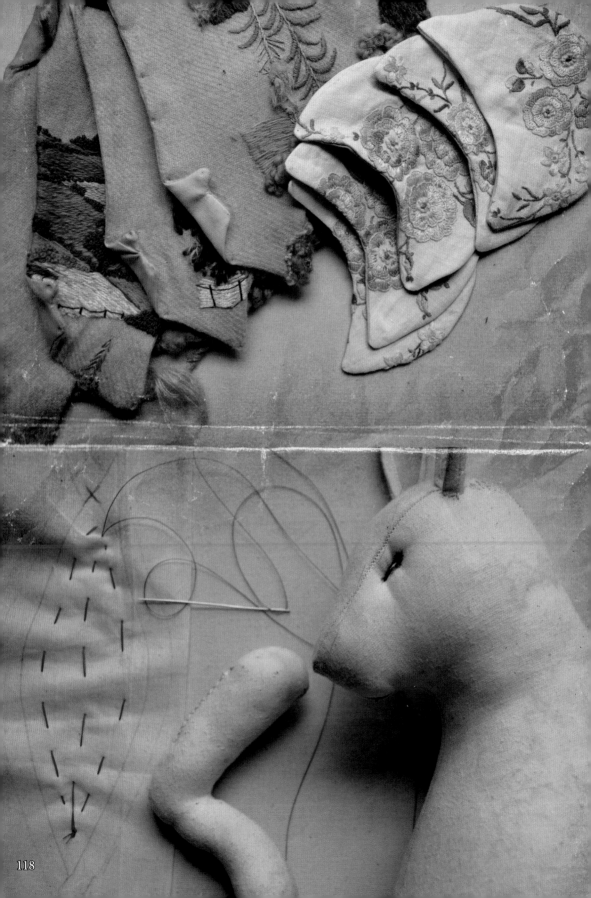

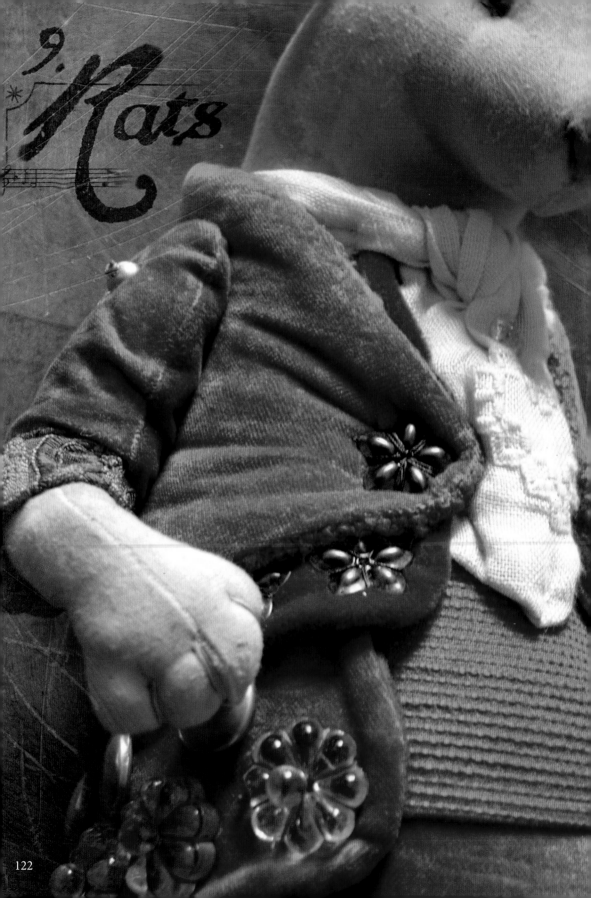

9. Hats

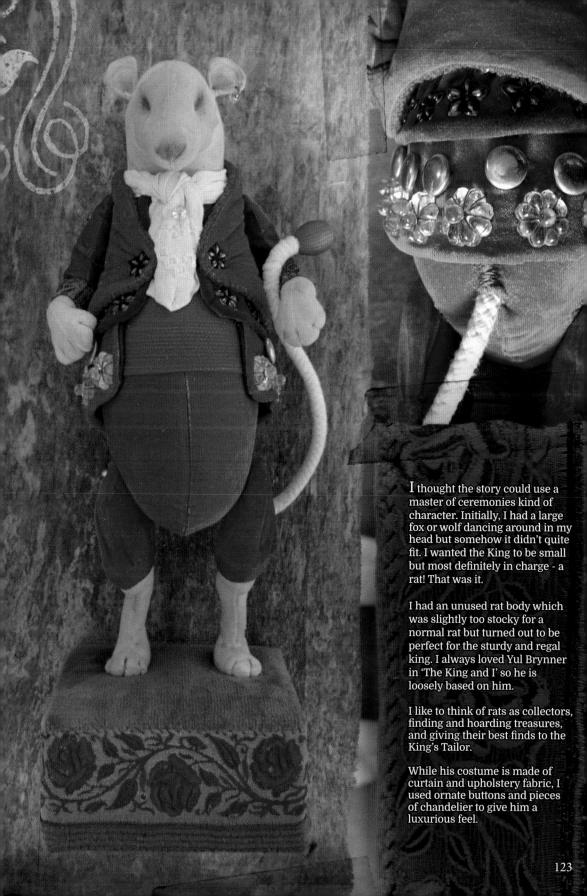

I thought the story could use a master of ceremonies kind of character. Initially, I had a large fox or wolf dancing around in my head but somehow it didn't quite fit. I wanted the King to be small but most definitely in charge - a rat! That was it.

I had an unused rat body which was slightly too stocky for a normal rat but turned out to be perfect for the sturdy and regal king. I always loved Yul Brynner in 'The King and I' so he is loosely based on him.

I like to think of rats as collectors, finding and hoarding treasures, and giving their best finds to the King's Tailor.

While his costume is made of curtain and upholstery fabric, I used ornate buttons and pieces of chandelier to give him a luxurious feel.

123

The Post Office Rats - these guys were just a blast to make; I had to stop myself from going slightly overboard and adding too many letters to their backpacks. They are quick and nimble, very bright and highly organised - perfect to cast as workers in the Wish Post offices. Like the badgers, their uniforms have little badges on them to show where they have worked. One of them is from Cannes, how fancy!

As they rush around so much I pictured them carrying their tails over their arms to keep them out of the way. A thimble on the tip prevents them getting trodden on or, worse, trapped under the wheel of a letter-laden trolley. Rats sometimes get a bad press so I wanted mine to

Those tails have a tale to tell - they drove me nuts! - but that's another story...

During the time I was making these, I was enthralled by the Beatrix Potter ballet so there's a tip of the hat to those costumes in the Squirrels' attire.

These two critters are bright and busy and in charge of sewing all the letters together for the Festival. They are rather precious about their scissors and balls of string - and the string cupboard keys aren't handed out to just *anyone*.

I originally imagined making five of our bushy-tailed friends but luckily stopped at two. Thank goodness I did - too many Squirrels with the string cupboard keys... things could have got ugly!

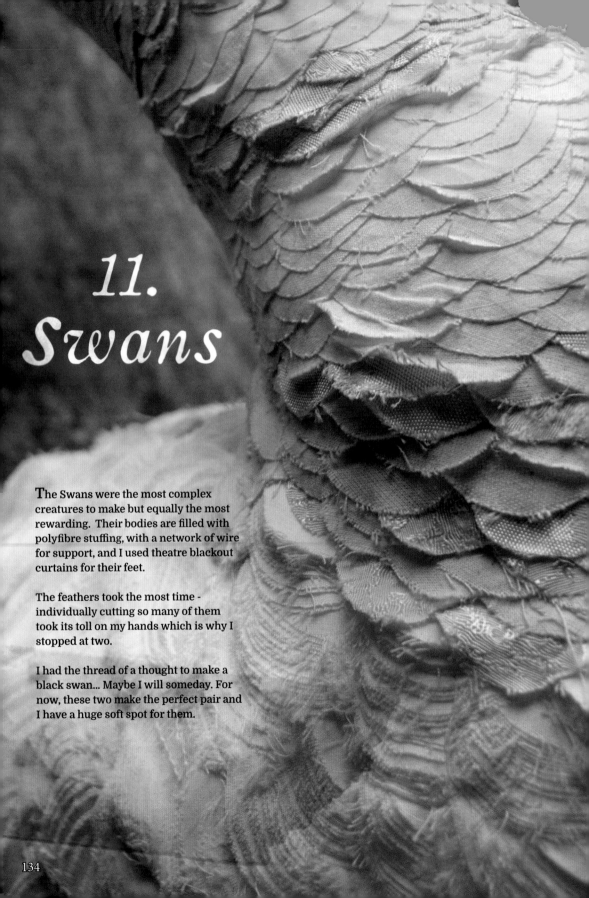

11.
Swans

The Swans were the most complex creatures to make but equally the most rewarding. Their bodies are filled with polyfibre stuffing, with a network of wire for support, and I used theatre blackout curtains for their feet.

The feathers took the most time - individually cutting so many of them took its toll on my hands which is why I stopped at two.

I had the thread of a thought to make a black swan... Maybe I will someday. For now, these two make the perfect pair and I have a huge soft spot for them.

12

TOADSTOOL POSTBOXES

The bases of the Toadstool Postboxes are made from vintage coffee grinders. As soon as I knew they were what I needed, the collecting began! I kept an eye out for ones that had been battered by the sands of time, the ones with rusted mechanisms, seemingly obsolete... those were my ground gold dust. Finding them in the most obscure places really was a thrill.

I hand painted them, enhancing their aged look, and gave them each their own official number. The tiny drawers are the perfect size for The Wish Post letters and the Toadstools sit perfectly upon the plinth-like shape. They really were a joy to make.

I considered making some in the style of a birdhouse - wouldn't it be fab to photograph them up in the trees? Maybe I still will.

INSPIRATION &
Acknowledgements

When I was asked to create an exhibition for Yorkshire Sculpture Park it provided a great opportunity for me not only to create a bigger collection than I normally would but also to bring together lots of ideas I've had for ages.

After years of making toadstools I realised I hadn't made many *fly agaric* ones (the typical red mushrooms with white spots), so I wanted to include these as part of the theme.

I came across a box of glass toadstool beads and was thinking of all the ways I could use them. While being very small, they were quite punchy in colour and character. Early on, I tried sewing them on some tiny animal jackets but they just didn't quite seem to fit.

When I played around with them as tiny hats for mice, however, they suddenly sparked lots of ideas and a backstory started to form quite quickly.

Who were the mice and why did they have hats on? Were they at a festival? And if so, what were they celebrating?

So the tiniest of beads started everything off. In the end, I used them very little but I think they work best as tiny mice hats, which I really adore.

As the idea for The Wish Post took shape, I knew I wanted it to feature a broad range of creatures, and for them to be brought to life in a picture book style story.

After designing and making all the creatures (pretty close to 2 years of sewing!) the prospect of creating the scenes for the book was a real breath of fresh air.

I am by no means a photographer but I am quite stubborn and like to do as much as I can myself.

Nearly all of the images were shot in my home and garden, with the larger sets (like the rats' sorting office) being built against the kitchen wall or constructed on the floor and then shot from above, with me standing precariously on the dinner table.

I can laugh about it now but it really wasn't the most ideal way of working - and throw two naughty cats into the process and... well, you can imagine.

Setting the story for the Wish Post in the here-and-now was important to me as I wanted it to be believable and relatable to a broad age group.

I think most of us can relate to experiencing a time where you've wished for something with all of your heart - really pined and longed for it - and then nothing happens for what seems like the longest time... so you just have to hold on and keep going.

I hope that the Tale of Poe the Mouse is a reminder of this in some way. Sometimes you have to hold faith in whatever things you can, even when it feels like you have to go backwards as well as forwards. And then sometimes all you can do is rest, and hope, and wait and see how things turn out.

...

Acknowledgements:

Big thanks to all my family and friends. Especially big thankyous to Mum and Dad, Amanda Peach, Graham Pilling, The Girl with the copper Kettle, Slimy 6 Linda and the Davies family, Jeffery Beatty Eldin, my far away USA chum R.A.S., and Dildy the Darly Beau.

MISTER FINCH
June 2018

About *the* Author

Mister Finch is a self-taught artist who lives in Leeds, UK, not too far from the beautiful Yorkshire Dales.

His charming textile creations are made of up-cycled materials, forgotten fabrics, and discarded bits and bobs.

With some know-how and a little bit of magic, the velvet curtains from an old hotel, a threadbare wedding dress, or a vintage apron are brought to life as wonderfully curious birds and beasts, looking for new homes and new adventures.